THE SESAME STREET TREASURY

Featuring Jim Henson's Sesame Street Muppets

VOLUME 5

STARRING
THE NUMBER
5
AND THE LETTERS
E AND F

Children's Television Workshop / Funk & Wagnalls, Inc.

WRITTEN BY:

Linda Bove with the National Theatre of the Deaf
Michael Frith
Jocelyn Gunnar
Jerry Juhl
Emily Perl Kingsley
Deborah Kovacs
Sharon Lerner
Jeffrey Moss
Robert Oksner
Ray Sipherd
Norman Stiles
Jon Stone
Daniel Wilcox

ILLUSTRATED BY:

Tom Cooke
Mel Crawford
Peter Cross
Larry DiFiori
Mary Grace Eubank
Michael Frith
Joe Mathieu
Marc Nadel
Michael J. Smollin
Maggie Swanson
Bob Taylor

PHOTOGRAPHS BY:

Charles Rowan
Neil Selkirk
View-Master International Group

Manufactured in the United States of America   5 6 7 8 9 0
ISBN: 0-8343-0052-4 (set); 0-8343-0057-5 (vol. 5)

Grover's Poem about Feelings

Sometimes I feel happy.
Sometimes I feel sad.
Sometimes I feel worried.
Sometimes I feel glad.
Sometimes I feel silly,
and I stand right on my head.

Sometimes I feel lazy,
and I cuddle up in bed.
Sometimes I feel little—
not much bigger than a bug.
But no matter what I'm feeling,
I feel better with a hug!

Too Much Farley, Too Little Sweater

One day, Grover was planting seeds in his garden. As he planted each seed, he talked to it:

"Hello there, little seed! You are going to grow into a great big plant someday."

Farley lived next door to Grover's garden. He looked out his window and watched Grover planting seeds. Farley called out:

"Hi, Grover! Can I help you plant those seeds?"

"Why certainly, little Farley! Do not forget to wear a sweater," said Grover. "It is just a little bit cold outside today."

Farley took out his favorite sweater. His grandmother had made it for him. Farley started to put on his sweater. Something was wrong! The hole in the top was too small for his head. The sleeves were too tight. The front of the sweater only came down to the middle of his stomach.

"Oh, no!" said Farley: "Something happened to my sweater! My sweater got all little. I can't wear my sweater anymore!" And Farley sat down on the floor and cried.

After a while, Grover began to wonder where Farley was. Grover went to Farley's house.

"What is wrong, little Farley?" asked Grover.

"Grover, somebody changed my sweater! It used to fit me. Now the hole is too small for my head, and the sleeves are too tight for my arms, and the sweater only comes down to the middle of my tummy. ... What's wrong with my sweater?" Farley was getting very sad.

Grover nodded his head. He knew what was wrong with Farley's sweater. He explained:

"Farley, do you know that the little tiny seeds that I plant outside will grow into great big plants?"

"Yeah," sniffed Farley.

"Well, seeds do not grow into plants overnight," said Grover. "They grow a little bit at a time until they are all grown up. People grow a little bit at a time, too. They start out very little. They grow a little tiny bit every day for many years. Then they are grown up."

"Is my sweater too small because I am growing up?" asked Farley.

"Of course! It is time for you to give your sweater to somebody who is smaller than you are," said Grover.

"Wow, Grover! How did you know this?" asked Farley.

"My mommy told me, when I got too big for the sweater *my* grandma made for me. Here is my old sweater. It will fit you. Now, let us go outside and plant these seeds."

And that's just what they did.

Joe Mathieu

mother

father

baby

brother

sister

MEET THE MONSTERS

You can see my family's photos
In our family photo book.
Take a minute now to notice
Just how much alike we look.

dog

cat

fish

grandmother,grandfather

We're a loving group of monsters.
We are gentle. We are kind.
You will find that we are friendly,
Which I'm sure you will not mind.

FIRE! FIRE!

There's a fire in the hot dog cart. Help Fireman Ernie get to the fire so he can put it out.

Sam Shows Big Bird Five

Betty Lou

Home:	456 Sesame Street
Favorite Food:	Cinnamon toast
Favorite Drink:	Fresh orange juice
Best Friend:	Luis
Pet:	Talbert the Goldfish
Favorite Activities:	Helping in the fix-it shop, playing baseball
Favorite Musical Instrument:	The xylophone
Favorite Clothes:	Overalls with lots of pockets
Favorite Wish:	To build a go-cart

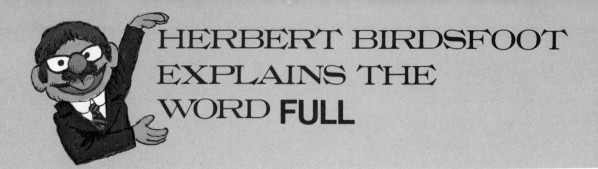

HERBERT BIRDSFOOT EXPLAINS THE WORD **FULL**

Hi, there. This is your friend, Herbert Birdsfoot. I'm here to tell you about the word **FULL**.

As you can see, this glass is **FULL**. It's **FULL** of yummy strawberry.

Strawberry soda?

Hey, *don't*.

NUMEROS   NUMBERS

Say it in Spanish!

uno
1 · one

dos
2 · two

tres
3 · three

cuatro
4 · four

cinco
5 · five

seis
6 · six

siete
7 · seven

ocho
8 · eight

nueve
9 · nine

diez
10 · ten

"Hi! Oscar the Grouch here. Great day for fishing, isn't it? Nothing better than sitting in a wet trash can that's rusty and yucchy. It's wonderful! I guess I like fishing most because of the slimy worms and smelly fish. What? It doesn't sound like fun to you? Well, go away then. I can't help it if you don't appreciate the icky things in life!"

On the Farm

farm

cow

horse

pig

rooster

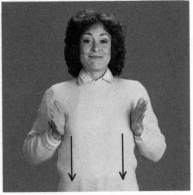

farmer

donkey

grow

corn

How many things in this picture can you "sign"?

I, Farmer Grover, must feed the horse.

The farmer

must

feed  the horse.

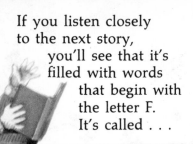If you listen closely to the next story, you'll see that it's filled with words that begin with the letter F. It's called . . .

F f

...The Fable of Fat Fireman Foster

O nce upon a time, there was a famous fireman named Fat Fireman Foster. Fat Fireman Foster was famous because he was a fabulous fire fighter and because all his names began with the letter F.

One Friday in February, Fat Fireman Foster was driving his fancy fire truck through a forest when all of a sudden he saw some smoke! "Where there's smoke, there's fire!" said Fat Fireman Foster. "And since this is a forest, that must be a forest fire! Never fear," called Fat Fireman Foster. "Fat Fireman Foster is here!"

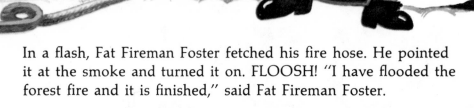

In a flash, Fat Fireman Foster fetched his fire hose. He pointed it at the smoke and turned it on. FLOOSH! "I have flooded the forest fire and it is finished," said Fat Fireman Foster.

But when the smoke cleared, Fat Fireman Foster found that it had not been a forest fire at all!

"Oh, no!" said Fat Fireman Foster. "I figured it was a forest fire—but it was a frankfurter fire instead! Just a few friendly folks fixing frankfurters! Oh, I'm sorry, folks," said Fat Fireman Foster. "Can you ever forgive me?"

"Sure, we'll forgive you!" said the folks. "We still have our frankfurters. And we have our fins and flippers, too. Fortunately we know how to swim and eat at the same time. Come join the fun, Fat Fireman Foster!"

So Fat Fireman Foster joined the fun and had a fabulous time feeding on frankfurters and flipping the flippers he borrowed from his new-found friends.

There are two things to be learned from the fable of Fat Fireman Foster:

Number one is:
Sometimes things are not
what you think they are.

Number two is:
The names Fat, Fireman,
and Foster all begin
with the letter F.

Do you know which food each friend loves to eat?

BIRD SEED

Figgy Fizz

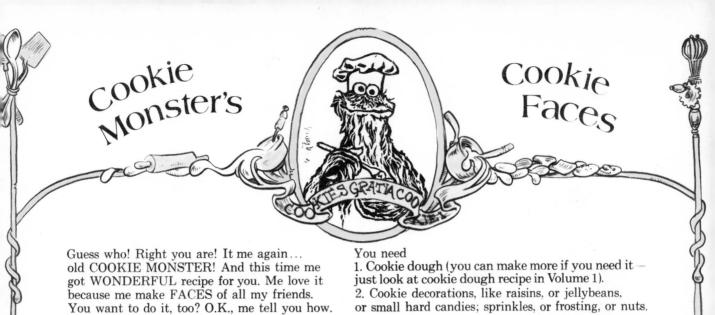

Cookie Monster's

Cookie Faces

Guess who! Right you are! It me again...
old COOKIE MONSTER! And this time me
got WONDERFUL recipe for you. Me love it
because me make FACES of all my friends.
You want to do it, too? O.K., me tell you how.

You need
1. Cookie dough (you can make more if you need it —
just look at cookie dough recipe in Volume 1).
2. Cookie decorations, like raisins, or jellybeans,
or small hard candies; sprinkles, or frosting, or nuts.

Sprinkle flour on cloth and roll out your
dough on it (about ¼ inch thick).

Now cut out face shapes and peel away
extra dough, like this...

Now decorate them.   Raisins make good hair and eyes. Jellybean make
VERY tasty nose. Here are some of
my COOKIE FRIENDS...

ERNIE
Red
jellybean
nose.

BERT
Orange
jellybean
nose.

GROVER
Pink
jellybean nose.
And sprinkles
make him look
fuzzy.

SUSAN and GORDON
Peanuts make good noses
for people.

Have a grownup heat oven to 400
degrees. Put in cookies, and wait
six to eight minutes. Oh, boy! Me
can hardly wait to have my
friends for dinner!

FRITH

Opposites

In   **Out**

Up   **Down**

Standing   **Sitting**

Open

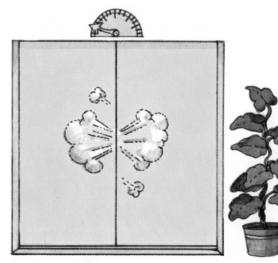

Closed

Sherlock Hemlock
in
The Case of the Lost Lunch

Boo-hoo!

E-Gad! A bird in distress! What is the matter, Little Bird?

Oh, Mr. Sherlock Hemlock, sir, my friend Big Bird invited me to his nest for a delicious birdseed lunch, and I don't know how to get there. And I'm getting VERY hungry.

Never fear, Little Bird. I, Sherlock Hemlock, the World's Greatest Detective, will help you find the way to Big Bird's nest.

Oh, look! There's a trail of birdseed on the ground. Maybe Big Bird dropped it on the way home from Mr. Hooper's store.

E-Gad!
A trail of birdseed!
Perhaps Big Bird dropped it on his way home from Mr. Hooper's store. If we follow it, we may find our way to Big Bird's nest.

Look! Mr. Hemlock...
(munch, munch)

MUNCH!
MUNCH!

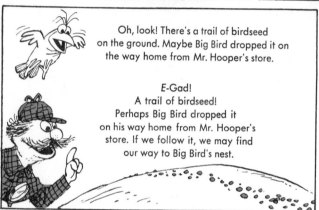

The birdseed leads...

(gobble, gobble)
UNDER this fence.

(smack, gulp)
Look—OVER the bridge...

(crunch, yum)
He must have gone
DOWN this hill...

(munch, crunch)
and UP these stairs...

(yum, yum) and IN this door...

(yum, yum)
and OUT that door...
and there he is!

HELP LITTLE BIRD FIND HIS WAY TO BIG BIRD'S NEST

All in the Family

Look at all of these sentences! The last word in each sentence is underlined. What is the last word? Look at the words next to each sentence. Find the word that matches the underlined word in the sentence.

It is the **fall.**

fall
call
hall

Oh, my! That is **tall.**

tall
ball
fall

I walk down the **hall.**

call
hall
tall

bounce a **ball.**

hall
ball
tall

It goes over a **wall.**

tall
call
wall

I make a phone **call.**

wall
ball
call

I say to my mommy: "My **ball** went over a **tall wall**, so I went down the **hall**, and I made this phone **call**. And that is **all**."

FIVE TOES

This little pig went to market;
This little pig stayed at home;
This little pig had roast beef;
This little pig had none;
This little pig cried,
"Wee, wee, wee!" all the way home.